Understanding Radiation Science:
Basic Nuclear and Health Physics

James Mannie Shuler

Universal Publishers
Boca Raton, Florida
USA • 2006

Understanding Radiation Science:
Basic Nuclear and Health Physics

Universal Publishers
Boca Raton, Florida • USA
2006

ISBN: 1-58112- 907-6

www.universal-publishers.com

TABLE OF CONTENTS

CHAPTER I

Introduction

The purpose of this book, *Understanding Radiation Science: Basic Nuclear and Health Physics*, is to provide the reader a basic understanding of radiation science. Therefore, basic nuclear physics and health physics principles are presented, including chapters on atomic structure, types of radiation, terminology and units, radiation biology, exposure and controls, background radiation, and personnel monitoring.

Radiation is the energy emitted from an atom in the form of particles or electromagnetic waves. Radiation (ionizing radiation), as used in this book, means alpha particles, beta particles, gamma rays, x-rays, and neutrons. These radiations will be defined later. It does not include non-ionizing radiation, such as radio waves, microwaves, or visible, infrared, or ultraviolet light.

Physics deals with understanding and explaining the behavior of matter and energy and the fundamental forces of nature that govern the interactions between particles In comparison, chemistry deals with the rearrangements of the atoms that form molecules and the analysis and synthesis of materials.

Nuclear physics is the branch of physics concerned with the nucleus of the atom. It is usually applied to nuclear energy and nuclear power. Whereas, atomic physics or atom physics is physics of the electron hull of atoms. Physicists distinguish between atomic physics (dealing with the effects of the electron hull and the nucleus's overall spin and electric charge) and nuclear physics (dealing with the forces within the atomic nuclei and reactions that alter, fuse or split them). Biophysics or biological physics is an interdisciplinary science that applies theories and methods of the physical sciences to questions of biology. Nuclear engineering is the practical application of the principles of nuclear physics and the interaction between radiation and matter.

Health physics is the profession devoted to the protection of man and his environment from unwarranted radiation exposure. *Exposure* means being exposed to ionizing radiation or to radioactive material. Therefore, a health physicist is a person engaged in the study of the problems and practice of providing radiation protection. He is concerned with an understanding of the mechanisms of radiation damage, with the development and implementation of methods and procedures necessary to evaluate radiation hazards, and with providing protection to man and his environment from unwarranted radiation exposure. Health physics encompasses many disciplines, including physics, biology, chemistry, and ecology.

Atomic Structure

Matter is composed of chemical elements such as oxygen, hydrogen, carbon or iron. The smallest piece that an element can be broken into and still retain its identity is called an atom. It is the fundamental building block of elements. Atoms of all elements are made of three basic particles. The proton carries one positive charge of electricity. The electron carries one negative charge of electricity. The neutron is electrically neutral or has no charge of electricity.

The protons and the neutrons form the densely packed nucleus of the atom around which revolves electrons. The electron is the smallest of the primary particles. It orbits around the atom's nucleus and is held in orbit by the attraction of the negative charge of the electron and the positive charge of the nucleus. The proton is about 1840 times larger than the electron. It is the positive charge of the proton that gives the nucleus of the atom an overall positive charge. The neutron is a neutral particle. Scientists believe that the neutron is composed of a proton and an electron. Since the charges will cancel each other out, the result is a neutral particle.

The nucleus of the atom is the mass in the center, around which the electrons rotate. Both the neutron and the proton are in the nucleus of the atom. The charge of the nucleus is electrically positive. The number of protons in the nucleus determines the strength of the net positive charge and the name of the element. For example, if the nucleus of an atom contained one proton, the element would be hydrogen. If another proton could be added to the nucleus, the element would be helium. Neutrons exist in the nucleus in different numbers, but have no effect on the element or its chemical properties.

Electron
Proton
Neutron

The atom is neutral, because it has the same number of electrons as protons. The number of protons or electrons of an atom is its atomic number, Z. This determines what chemical element the atom is. For example, hydrogen has an atomic number of one and helium has an atomic number of two. All atoms of the same element have the same number of protons in the nucleus, but they can have different numbers of neutrons and still be atoms of the same element. If the nucleus of an element has more neutrons in it than another nucleus of the same element, that atom with more neutrons in its nucleus will be heavier. The number of neutrons in the nucleus is denoted by N. The total number of protons and neutrons in the nucleus is the atomic weight or atomic mass of an atom. The atomic mass of the nucleus, A, *is* equal to $Z + N$.

$$\frac{\text{Atomic mass } (A)}{\text{Atomic number } (Z)} \text{Element} = {}^{239}_{94}\text{Pu}$$

The term ^{239}Pu means the atom of plutonium with an atomic weight of 239. Since the atomic number of plutonium is 94, it has 94 protons in the nucleus. 239-94=145. So there are 145 neutrons in the nucleus of ^{239}Pu. Since the number of neutrons has no effect on the atomic number or the chemical properties of the atom, an atom with one proton is hydrogen whether it has one, two or three neutrons. Atoms of the same

6

chemical element having different numbers of neutrons are called isotopes of the element. All isotopes of an element have the same atomic number but different atomic weights.

An atom normally has the same number of orbiting electrons as it has protons in the nucleus. Every element has a different number of electrons orbiting around the nucleus. It is the number of electrons and their orbit that determines the chemical properties of the element.

Some elements have an excess of either protons or neutrons in their nucleus. These elements are unstable. These unstable elements seek stability by emitting either particles of matter or electromagnetic energy. In radiating or emitting this excess energy as ionizing radiation, the atoms become a different element or a lower energy (more stable) form of the original element

CHAPTER II

Types of Radiation

The nucleus of an atom is normally stable, but some atoms have unstable nuclei. These unstable nuclei are called radioactive atoms. They are at an excited or highly energetic state. When the atom drops from an unstable state to a stable state, energy is given off. This energy is radiation and may be in the form of electromagnetic energy or the ejection of particles from the nucleus. This radiation may be gamma, x-ray, beta, alpha or neutron radiation.

Ernest Rutherford discovered that uranium compounds produce three different kinds of radiation in 1899. He named them α alpha, β beta, and γ gamma radiation. He separated the radiations according to their penetrating abilities with alpha being the least penetrating, gamma being the most penetration, and beta falling between.

X-rays are penetrating electromagnetic radiations whose wave lengths are shorter than visible light. X-rays are produced by bombarding a metallic target with fast electrons in a vacuum. As orbital electrons fall from a higher to lower energy orbital shell, energy is released in the form of electromagnetic radiation.

Gamma rays are short wavelength electromagnetic radiations emitted from the nucleus of an atom. Gamma rays are the same as x-rays except they originate in the nucleus of the atom instead of the electron cloud. It is customary to refer to electromagnetic energy originating in the nucleus as gamma rays, and those originating in the electron shell as x-rays. All electromagnetic radiations travel at the velocity of light, which is about 3×10^8 meters per second (m/s). The gamma ray is a highly penetrating type of nuclear radiation. Gamma rays or photons do not consist of particles, have no mass, travel at the speed of light, and do not lose their energy as rapidly as either alpha or beta particles. Gammas produce no direct ionization by collision as alpha and beta particles, because gamma photons have no mass. They are absorbed or lose their energy by three processes known as the photoelectric effect, the Compton effect, and pair production.

Beta particle is emitted from the nucleus of an atom, with a mass and charge equal in magnitude to those of the electron. In other words, a beta particle is an electron that originates in the nucleus of an atom. A neutron consists of a proton and an electron that combined to form electrically neutral particle. When a neutron decays in the nucleus, it may eject the electron. This high speed electron is a beta particle. The neutron in the nucleus becomes just a proton, and the atom's atomic number increases by one. The atom weight of the atom remains the same. Beta particles are less penetrating than gamma rays or x-rays, but more than alpha particles. The beta particle does not lose its energy as rapidly as the alpha particle. This is because the beta particle a very small particle, has less charge than the alpha particle, and is moving at a higher rate of speed. The range of velocities for beta particles ranges from about 25 to 95 percent of the speed of light. The range of the beta particle is approximately inversely proportional to the density of the material through which it passes. Beta particle has little penetrating power. It has a range in air from less than an inch to several feet. It can be stopped by a board of inch or by a 1/8 inch of aluminum.

Alpha particle consists of two protons and two neutrons ejected from the unstable nucleus. This particle has a net charge of plus two. The alpha particle is equal in charge and mass to the nucleus of a helium atom. Since the alpha particle consists of two neutrons, the emission of an alpha particle will decrease the atomic weight by four and will decrease the atomic number by two. Alpha particles are comparatively large, heavy particles of matter which have been ejected from the nucleus of a radioactive material with a very high velocity. Alpha particles lose their energy rapidly and hence have a limited range. They travel only about 6 or 7 centimeters in air. The alpha particle is the least penetrating of the three common forms of radiation, being stopped by a sheet of paper. It is not dangerous to living things unless the alpha-emitting substance is inhaled or ingested or comes into contact with the lens of the eye. Then they are very harmful.

When an alpha or beta particle is emitted, the atomic number changes because the chemical properties of an atom are determined by that atom's atomic number. The ejection of a particle (alpha or beta) and/or energy (gamma rays) from the nucleus is call disintegration.

Neutron radiation is usually caused by some outside force affecting the nucleus. The nuclei of an atom may be bombarded by an alpha or beta particle causing the emission of a neutron. One of the most important methods of neutron radiation production is fission. Fission is the splitting of a nucleus into two or more other nuclei and the release of a relatively large amount of energy. In addition to the fission-product nuclei, some individual neutrons are also released. So when fission occurs, fission products are created, and neutrons and energy are released. For all practical purposes, only a small number of "heavy" atomic nuclei are fissionable. The best-known fissionable atoms are ^{235}U and ^{239}Pu. Spontaneous fission is when a nucleus undergoes fission without outside help. This is also a source of neutrons and energy. Neutrons and energy are also produced by fusion. This is when two light atomic nuclei are joined together to form a single heavier nucleus. Neutron radiation is very penetrating. This radiation is readily shielded by about a foot of material that contains a large percentage of hydrogen atoms, such as water or polyethylene. Neutron radiation at very high energies has the ability to make other materials radioactive if they absorb neutrons.

CHAPTER III

Terminology and Units

The properties of radiation and radioactivity are measured in certain units. There are several units of radiation quantity. It is impossible to measure a quantity of radiation directly, since it can bring about a change in matter only to the extent of the energy that is absorbed by this matter.

Dose measurement terminology and definitions are important to understand and use properly. Radioactivity has its own specific terminology and definitions, as well. The different terms that are used with dose and its measurement and radioactivity and its measurement are presented below.

One must understand and use these terms precisely to convey the proper meaning in the radiation sciences. This is very important. Serious mistakes can result from improper use of terminology. Most of the following definitions come from regulatory sources.

15

Dose Measurements

Dose or *radiation dose* is a generic term that means absorbed dose, dose equivalent, effective dose equivalent, committed dose equivalent, committed effective dose equivalent, or total effective dose equivalent, as defined in other paragraphs of this chapter.

Occupational dose means the dose received by an individual in the course of employment in which the individual's assigned duties involve exposure to radiation or to radioactive material. Occupational dose does not include doses received from background radiation, from any medical administration the individual has received, from exposure to individuals administered radioactive material in voluntary participation in medical research programs, or as a member of the public. *Public dose* means the dose received by a member of the public from exposure to radiation or to radioactive material released by a licensee, or to any other source of radiation under the control of a licensee. Public dose does not include occupational dose or doses received from background radiation, from any medical administration the individual has received, from exposure to individuals administered radioactive material in voluntary participation in medical research programs.

External dose means that portion of the dose equivalent received from radiation sources outside the body, and *internal* dose means that portion of the dose equivalent received from radioactive material taken into the body. *Absorbed dose* means the energy imparted by ionizing radiation per unit mass of irradiated material. The units of absorbed dose are the rad and the gray (Gy).

The *roentgen* (R) is a unit for measuring gamma rays or x-rays only. This unit measures x-ray or gamma radiation in terms of the charge deposited in one unit volume of air. One roentgen equals 2.58×10^{-4} coulomb per kilogram of air.

The *rad*, radiation absorbed dose, is a quantity of any type of ionizing radiation in terms of the energy absorbed per unit mass of material. The rad is the unit of absorbed dose equal to 0.01 Joules per kilogram in any medium.

The *gray* (Gy) is the International System of Units (SI) unit used to measure a quantity called absorbed dose. One gray is equivalent to an absorbed dose of 1 Joule/kilogram or 100 rad. Absorbed dose is often expressed in terms of hundredths of a gray, or centigrays (cGy).

17

Dose equivalent (H_T) means the product of the absorbed dose in tissue, quality factor, and all other necessary modifying factors at the location of interest. The units of dose equivalent are the rem and sievert (Sv).

Since roentgen measures radiation in air only, it cannot be used to measure to biological effects on man. One reason is radiation acts differently in air and tissue. The *rem*, roentgen equilavent man, is used to measure the biological effects of radiation. It is a special unit of dose equivalent. The dose equivalent in rems in numerically equal to the absorbed dose in rads multiplied by the quality factor (QF), the distribution factor, and any other necessary modifying factors.

The *Sievert* (Sv) is the International System of Units (SI) unit used to derive a quantity called equivalent dose. Equivalent dose is often expressed in terms of millionths of a Sievert, or microsievert (mSv). To determine equivalent dose (Sv), you multiply absorbed dose (Gy) by a quality factor (QF) that is unique to the of incident radiation. One Sievert is equivalent to 100 rem.

The *quality factor* (QF) is the linear-energy transfer-dependent factor by which the absorbed dose (rad) is multiplied to obtain a quantity that expresses the effectiveness of the absorbed dose on a common scale for all ionizing radiations. For most beta or gamma radiation, the QF is 1. So 1 rad is equal to 1 rem. The rem is actually defined as the amount of any type of ionizing radiation which produces the same biological effect as 1 rad of gamma radiation. An R is also about equal to 1 rad or 1 rem for gamma radiation.

Since the R, the rad, and the rem are rather large quantities of radiation, they may be subdivided into smaller units. The "m" is an abbreviation for "milli-", a prefix that means one-thousandth of.one milliroentgen (mR), millirad (mrad) and millirem (mrem) are one-thousandths of these radiations. The units of radiation measurement discussed above are used to express the dose. The dose is a quantity of radiation received by material. The rate at which the radiation is received is called the dose rate. So dose will be written as mR, mrad, or mrem. The dose rate will be expressed as mR/hr., mrad/hr.or mrem/hr.

The *collective dose* is the sum of the individual doses received in a given period of time by a specified population from exposure to a specified source of radiation. The *committed dose equivalent* ($H_{T,50}$) means the dose equivalent to organs or tissues of reference (T) that will be received from an intake of radioactive material by an individual during the 50-year period following the intake. The *committed effective dose equivalent* ($H_{E,50}$) is the sum of the products of the weighting factors applicable to each of the body organs or tissues that are irradiated and the committed dose equivalent to these organs or tissues ($H_{E,50} = \Sigma W_T H_{T,50}$). The *effective dose equivalent* (H_E) is the sum of the products of the dose equivalent to the organ or tissue (H_T) and the weighting factors (W_T) applicable to each of the body organs or tissues that are irradiated ($H_E = \Sigma W_T H_T$).

Total Effective Dose Equivalent (TEDE) means the sum of the deep-dose equivalent (for external exposures) and the committed effective dose equivalent (for internal exposures). *Shallow-dose equivalent* (Hs), which applies to the external exposure of the skin of the whole body or the skin of an extremity, is taken as the dose equivalent at a tissue depth of 0.007 centimeter (7 mg/cm^2).

The *weighting factor* W_T, for an organ or tissue (T) is the proportion of the risk of stochastic effects resulting from irradiation of that organ or tissue to the total risk of stochastic effects when the whole body is irradiated uniformly.

Radioactivity

The *Becquerel* (Bq) is the International System of Units (SI) unit used to measure radioactivity. One Becquerel is that quantity of a radioactive material that will have 1 transformation in one second (1 dps or 1 d/s), also written one Becquerel=1 disintegration per second (s^{-1}). There are 3.7×10^{10} Bq in one Curie. Radioactivity is often expressed in larger units like: thousands (kBq), millions (MBq) or even billions (GBq) of a Becquerel.

The *curie*, Ci, is a measure of radiation activity on how fast the radioactive substance is giving off radiation. One curie of any radioactive material is the amount of the material in which 3.7×10^{10} atoms disintegrate per second (dps or d/s). Each disintegration of an atom is really the emission of radiation by its unstable nucleus. If one has some radioactive material like plutonium and it produces 3.7×10^{10} alpha particles each second, then one has one curie of plutonium. Therefore, one curie=3.7×10^{10} disintegrations per second=3.7×10^{10} becquerels=2.22×10^{12} disintegrations per minute. Since a curie is a large amount of radiation, the terms millicurie (mCi) and microcurie (μCi) are often used. A millicurie (mCi) is one thousanth of a curie (3.7×10^{7}

21

disintegrations per second). A microcurie (μCi) is one millionth of a curie (3.7×10^4 disintegrations per second).

The amount of time it takes for one half of the atoms in an amount of radioactive material to decay or disintegrate is called the *half-life* of the radioactive material. A radioactive substance is continually giving off radioactive particles, so the amount of activity is decreasing. Eventually, the material will all disappear and there will not be any radioactivity. If the half-life of an isotope is very short, the material will disintegrate very quickly. The half-life is a characteristic property of each radioactive isotope. For example, Iodine-131 (^{131}I) has a half-life of 8 days, but Plutonium-239 (^{239}Pu) has a half-life of 24,390 years.

Disintegration per minute (dpm or d/m) is a unit describing the number of atoms that are disintegrating each minute in a radioactive source. *Counts per minute* (cpm or c/m) is the number of disintegrations in a radioactive source actually detected by a radiation detection instrument.

Since radiation is emitted in all directions from a source, the probes of most instruments cannot receive the results of all the disintegrations. The ratio between the number of disintegrations detected per minute (cpm) and the number of disintegrations taking place per minute (dpm) is the *counting efficiency* of the detecting instrument or cpm/dpm. The inverse of the counting efficiency (dpm/cpm) is the *correction factor* for the radiation detection instrument.

CHAPTER IV

Exposure and Controls

Radiation is almost always damaging to the cells or tissue of the body. Radiation injures or kills human cells, and is one reason that concentrated radiation doses are directed at cancer growth areas in the body. The reason for this is to kill or damage the cancerous tissue so that the growth and multiplication of the cancer is stopped.

Two types of effects of radiation on the human body are somatic and genetic effects. A *somatic* or *stochastic* risk are those health risks for which the probability of an occurrence, rather than the severity, is considered to be a function of dose without threshold and is limited to the exposed individual.

Somatic effects are called physical or observable effects and are the effects of large doses of radiation. This can medically be seen as red blood cell depression and radiation sickness. No somatic effects can be seen with an acute dose of 25 rem or less. The federally established exposure guides restrict the occupational exposure to radiation to an average of less than 5 rem per year. This is below the point of any measurable effect to the body. The most sensitive areas of the body include the reproductive organs and the organs in the trunk of the body. The least sensitive areas include the extremities, skin and muscles. Therefore, if the trunk can be shielded, the body is better protected against radiation. The genetic effects are the long range hereditary effects of radiation. *Nonstochastic effect* means health effects, the severity of which varies with the dose and for which a threshold is believed to exist. Radiation-induced cataract formation is an example of a nonstochastic effect (also called a deterministic effect).

Since radiation can have harmful effects on the human body, it is necessary to have operational controls to limit the amount of radiation an employee receives. These controls are established to keep personnel exposure below the minimum point at which significant damage may result. Operational controls are designed very conservatively so that an employee may work all his life around radiation without receiving enough radiation to cause harmful effects.

Exceeding operating controls is serious only when it is done continually or when the controls are exceeded by a great amount. The first control is for the whole body penetrating exposure. Gamma and neutrons are very penetrating and may reach and effect internal organs as the blood-forming tissue. The employer must maintain an adequate exposure record system to prevent exceeding the limits.

The skin or derma dose is the dose due to radiation penetrating enough to reach the living layer of skin. This is the sum of the beta, gamma and the neutron radiations. Since alpha radiation cannot even penetrate the dead layer of skin on the body, there is no dose for alpha radiations. There is a control for extremity exposure. The hands, forearms, feet and ankles are insensitive enough to receive more than the rest of the body. The extremity dose is the sum of the beta, gamma and neutron radiations.

An adult who is exposed to ionizing radiation in the course of work and is under a federal or state approved radiation protection program is a *radiation worker*. The annual limit for occupational dose to individual adult radiation workers can not exceed the most limiting value of (a) 5 rems (0.05 Sv) for the total effective dose equivalent, or

(b) the sum of the deep-dose equivalent and the committed dose equivalent to any individual organ or tissue, other than the lens of the eye, being equal to 50 rems (0.5 Sv). The annual limit to the lens of the eye is 15 rems (0.15 Sv). The annual limit for a shallow-dose equivalent is 50 rem (0.5 Sv) to the skin of the whole body or to the skin of any extremity.

The total effective dose equivalent to individual members of the public must not exceed 0.1 rem (1 mSv) in a year, exclusive of the dose contributions from background radiation, from any medical administration the individual has received, from exposure to individuals administered radioactive material and released, from voluntary participation in medical research programs, and from the disposal of radioactive material into sanitary sewerage. The dose in any unrestricted area from external sources, exclusive of the dose contributions from patients administered radioactive material and released, does not exceed 0.002 rem (0.02 millisievert) in any one hour.

28

CHAPTER V

Radiation Biology

Radiation biology deals with the effects of radiation on living organisms. In health physics the principle concern is with the effects of radiation on human beings. Exposure to radiation results in effects that range from no discernable effect to death of the person exposed. There are two basic reactions of human tissue that have been exposed to radiation. The atoms or molecules may be ionized by nuclear interactions. Ionization may also occur from the transformation of kinetic energy into thermal energy. Ionization is the process by which a neutral atom or molecule acquires a positive or negative charge. As ionization occurs, the ion pairs exhibit the natural propensity to recombine to restore electrical neutrality. This recombination may occur between the pairs originally created, or by the combination with other atoms or

29

molecules. In most cases, the latter occurs. Human tissue is composed of many complex chemical compounds, each of which is important to the proper function of the organism. Alteration of these compounds by ionization and recombination affects the ability of the organism to function, and may result in damage lethal to the organism. These are the changes that are of interest.

Radiation biology can best be understood when examined on an individual cell basis. The cell is composed of three major parts: the nucleus, the cytoplasm and the membranes. The membranes separate the nucleus from the cytoplasm and the cytoplasm from other cells.

The nucleus of a cell is the control center for cell function. It is normally located in the approximate center of the cell. The main component of the nucleus is the chromosomes and their constituent parts, the genes. The chromosomes (and the genes) are constructed of elaborate organic chemicals called amino acids. Proper function of the cell requires that the chromosomes and genes remain in a specific organization and the chemical linkages of the amino acids assure this.

Ionization of chemical elements in the amino acids or the molecular components disrupts the ability of the nucleus to control cell functions. The major functions that may be disturbed are metabolism growth and reproduction. Disturbance of metabolism affects the ability of the cell to absorb oxygen and nutrients and eliminate waste products. Such changes result in rather rapid death of the cell. Disrupted growth of the cell normally affects its ability to mature properly and carry out its assigned function. In this case, early death of the cell is usually also observed.

Disturbance of the ability of the cell to reproduce results in malformed daughter cells. Such malformation may result in death of the daughter cells or alter their function so that they do not perform in the pattern prescribed by the parent. These changes are caused by rearrangement of the genetic code which is traceable to radiation induced chemical disturbance of the chromosomes. Fortunately, most chromosome changes are lethal to the affected cell. In some cases, however, they may cause abnormal growth patterns ultimately resulting in the formation of benign or cancerous tumors. When they occur in germ cells (reproductive cells), it may result in neonatal death or abnormalities in the organisms formed by the mating of affected germ cells. Such abnormalities may be benign (neither advantageous nor deleterious) cause growth defects, or remain in the structure of the following germ cells to cause defects in future generations.

The cytoplasm is a more or less colorless liquid substance composed of elaborate compounds formed of carbon, hydrogen and oxygen. The chemicals carry out the function of the cell which varies according to the type of cell it is. The membrane can be equated to the skin of the cell. It is through the membrane that nutrients are absorbed and waste products of metabolism eliminated. It also serves as a physical barrier which maintains the integrity of the individual cell. Chemical disruption of either the cytoplasm or the cell membrane alters the metabolism of the cell or destroys its physical structure, either of which is normally lethal to the cell.

Radiation damage to individual cells affects not only those cells but may upset the function of the total human organism. The degree of functional upset varies drastically and is related to the amount of radiation exposure, the type of cells that have been irradiated, and the time period over which exposure occurred.

At very low radiation exposures there is no noticeable effect on large populations of humans. The changes noted are very similar to those observed from the normal aging process. Irradiated cells are not numerous and when they die, they are replaced by healthy cells which assume the functions of the dead cell. Since cells are subject to damage by chemicals encountered in routine living, as well as exposure from background sources of radiation, there is no discernable damage.

At slightly higher radiation exposure levels such as that experienced by radiation workers, more changes may be expected. However, since the population of people exposed is comparatively small, no observable effects are expected in that population.

With high levels of radiation exposure, the body may not be able to repair or replace damaged cells quickly enough, or such damage will affect a significant number of cells of particular organs such that there is an observable effect on the total organism, up to and including death.

Thus, the effects of radiation on humans range from no observable damage to damage that is immediately lethal. Further, there may be latent effects that are debilitating or lethal to the individual over the course of his lifetime. Examples may be damage to an organ causing improper or inadequate function, and formation of a lethal tumor.

There are two categories of biological manifestation of radiation damage to humans, somatic effects and genetic effects. These have been described earlier, but are clearly classified in this paragraph. Somatic effects are those biological effects which affect only the exposed individual. They include both direct cell damage and genetic alternations of cells of body tissues. These changes may be observed immediately or may be delayed for many years as is the case with radiation induced tumors. However, since the damage is limited to the lifetime of the individual, they are considered short term effects. The cells that are involved are termed somatic cells.

Genetic effects are those mutations which affect only the germ cells. These effects are not manifested in the exposed individual, but are carried on to future generations. Thus such effects are hereditary and are considered long term effects.

Acute radiation exposure of an individual may be generally defined as an exposure given in a short period of time. Acute radiation syndrome results from exposure of the whole body or a substantial part of the body, and runs a roughly predictable course over a period of time varying from a few hours to several weeks. The severity of the illness will depend on the magnitude of the dose, the radiosensitivity of the individual and to some extent on the parts of the body exposed. Early work by pioneers in radiation effects resulted in the general observation that the radiosensitivity of cells is directly proportional to their mitotic rate, and inversely proportional with their degree of differentiation. Since this early work, other factors have been found which affect radiosensitivity. Among these are the metabolic state of the cell, the state of cell division, and the state of nourishment.

It is obvious, then, that the probability of radiation damage to a cell or group of similar cells varies considerably. In the body, bone marrow, lymphoid tissues and reproductive organ cells rank among the most radiosensitive. Muscle and bone cells are the least radiosensitive. While it is not totally correct to classify radiation exposure by clinically observable effects since the body is a complex and highly interdependent organism, a general classification is useful in the assessment of the degree of acute exposure and determining treatment that should be accorded the exposed person. Such evaluations rely on the knowledgeable collection of body specimens from the exposed, and an objective log detailing onset of various symptoms.

It is appropriate for health physics personnel to be aware of the possible progress of the acute radiation syndrome so as to assist medical personnel in preparing a meaningful early exposure estimate so that timely treatment can be given. The general pattern which may be observed is listed below in the approximate order in which they may be observed by increasing radiation exposure to an individual.

1. Leukopenia - Reduced white cell count due to damage to the bone marrow.

2. Nausea, Vomiting

3. Internal Hemorrhage, Infection, Diarrhea - Damage to the walls of capillaries, intestinal walls and invasion of injured tissue by systemic bacteria.

4. Epilation - Loss of hair on portions of body exposed to radiation, occasionally accompanied by visible damage and deterioration of the skin and surface tissue.

5. Prostration, Disorientation - Shock or death, the final break down of body processes which may be attributed to progressive deterioration of vital functions or destruction of the nervous system.

The following is a breakdown of the exposures be related to expected effects:

1. Initial detectable clinical effects (leukopenia) is greate than 25 rem exposure (normally the threshold for clinical detection is 50 rem, but varies with the individual.)

2. LD_{50} (death of 50 percent of exposed) - 300 to 500 rem 3. LD_{100} (death of 100 percent of exposed) - is greater than 1000 rem exposure (This assumes full medical treatment can be afforded. Without treatment, the LD_{100} is greater than 600 rem exposure.)

Radiation sickness or radiation syndrome is a serious illness that occurs when the entire body, or most of it, receives a high dose of radiation over a short period of time. Usually the dose is greater than 50 rem.

There are four stages of radiation sickness. The first stage is the prodromal stage. In this stage the symptoms are nausea, vomiting, and possibly diarrhea that occur from minutes to days following exposure. These symptoms may last from minutes up to several days. The latent stage is next where the patient looks and feels generally healthy for a few hours or even up to a few weeks. In the overt or manifest illness stage, the symptoms depend on the specific dose

37

received and last from hours up to several months. The final stage is recovery or death.

There are three radiation syndromes: the bone marrow syndrome (or hematologic syndrome), the gastrointestinal (GI) syndrome, and the cardiovascular (CV) or central nervous system (CNS) syndrome.

The bone marrow syndrome is characterized by anorexia (lack of appetite), fever, and malaise. There is a drop in all blood cell counts for several weeks. The primary cause of death is infection and hemorrhage. The chance of survival decreases with increasing dose of radiation.

The GI syndrome is more severe. It includes severe diarrhea, fever, dehydration, and imbalance in the electrolytes (sodium, potassium, etc). Death is due to infection, dehydration and electrolyte imbalance and usually occurs within 2 weeks of exposure.

The CV/CNS syndrome is the most severe. There is initially extreme nervousness; confusion; severe nausea, vomiting, and watery diarrhea; burning sensations of the skin; and loss of consciousness. After the latent period, 5 to 6 hours after exposure there is return of watery diarrhea, convulsions, and coma and death comes within 3 days of exposure.

The observed effects of acute radiation exposures are related to radiosensitivity of the affected cells. The cells that are most radiosensitive are those undergoing mitosis, or cell division. It follows that the organs composed of cells which divide most rapidly are the most radiosensitive. Examples are bone marrow (and other blood forming organs), lymphoid tissue, and reproductive organs.

Finally, one should be cautioned that persons which have been subject to high radiation should be separated from other like patients as soon as feasible. It has been observed that if segregation does not occur, nausea and vomiting seem to be precipitated by a mass psychological reaction. This situation confuses evaluation of persons with relatively low exposure, making them appear to have received more exposure than they actually have. While such segregation presents early handling problems, it alleviates treatment requirements by reducing the number of persons requiring hospitalization and close care and secreting.

CHAPTER VI

Background Radiation

For the nuclear or health physicist to determine unwarranted radiation exposure, he must understand types of radiation and atomic structure. Man has always been exposed to ionizing radiation. This natural source of exposure to ionizing radiation is often referred to as "background radiation." Studies of the nature and origin of this source of exposure to man have revealed five main components: cosmic radiation, the radioactive materials in the earth's surface, in the air, in the water and in the human body. One might add that a man-made source, fall- out from nuclear weapons testing, influences the contribution from some of these sources. Although the amount which each of these factors contributes varies with the locale, each locale will have some background radiation. The study of these factors throughout the world is of value for a number of reasons.

Foremost among these is that the use of such data provides a basis of standard from which allowable exposure limits for radiation workers may be developed. In areas where background levels are much higher because of larger concentrations, knowledge may be gained about human hereditary effects at these increased levels. Such data is also needed in assessing the impact on or contribution of a nuclear facility to the existing population in a given area. In the design of building and/or shielding for low-level work, it is of value to know the radioactive contents of the substances used. Often levels inside a building are higher than the levels outside of the building because this factor has been neglected. Because of these needs, much data about background levels in many areas of the world have been acquired. Man has always lived with radiation, but now he is increasing his exposure to radiation by use of medical x-rays, color television, atomic weapons and atomic power plants. Radiation is not something new or something to be afraid of. It is understood and controlled and is used for the betterment of mankind.

Cosmic Radiation

Much work has been carried out in the study of cosmic radiation. This factor in background levels was discovered during attempts to reduce counter backgrounds. Though detection devices showed a response even in the absence of any known sources, it was assumed this background was due entirely to traces of radioactive substances in the air and ground. Thus, if a detector were elevated to a greater height above the earth's surface, the background would be greatly reduced. The use of balloons carrying ion chambers (a type of radiation detector) to great heights yield data which showed the effect increased, rather than decreased. This and other data showed that radiation was coming from outer space. The name "cosmic rays" was given to this high-energy, extraterrestrial radiation. Further study has shown that cosmic radiation consists of two parts: primary and secondary.

The primary component may be further divided into galactic, geomagnetically trapped radiation, and solar. The galactic cosmic rays come from outside the solar system and are composed mostly of positively charged particles. Studies have shown that outside the earth's atmosphere cosmic rays consist of mostly protons with some alpha particle must have a certain momentum. Otherwise, it may be trapped by the earth's magnetic field. This gives rise to the second type of the primary component cosmic rays.

Cosmic rays are the geomagnetically trapped radiation that consists of two belts of radiation (electrons and protons) which are observed at high altitudes. These belts are symmetrical with respect to the equator. These belts of radiation are being studied because of the dose rates to space travelers.

Solar cosmic rays are produced following severe solar flares on the surface of the sun. These rays consist of protons. These events are classed as high energy or low energy. The high energy events can be observed by ground level neutron detection devices. The low energy events are more frequent but must be detected at a high altitude. Since these events produce radiation throughout the solar system, they are of great importance in shielding design for manned space missions.

Secondary cosmic rays result from interactions which occur when the primary rays reach the earth's atmosphere. When the high energy particles collide with atoms of the atmosphere, many products are emitted: electrons, protons, neutrons, and other products called mesons and photons. These, in turn, produce other secondaries as they collide with matter or decay on the way toward the earth's surface. Thus, a multiplication or shower occurs in which as many as 10^8 secondaries may result from a single primary. Most of the primary rays are absorbed in the upper atmosphere. At the earth's surface, the secondary cosmic rays consist of mesons mainly (hard component), electrons and photons (soft component), and neutrons and protons (nucleonic component). At sea level, about seventy-five percent of the cosmic ray intensity is due to the hard component, mesons.

Mesons are one of a class of medium-mass, short-lived elementary particles with a mass between that of the electron and that of the proton. A photon is a quantity of electromagnetic energy. The dose rate produced by this source of background may be divided into two parts. The portion caused by direct ionizing component and the portion caused by the neutron component. The total dose rate at sea level would be about 50 mrem per year.

Terrestrial Radiation

Terrestrial radioactivity or the radioactive materials found in soil and rocks vary widely with the locale. The main contribution to background is the gamma ray dose from radioactive elements of the uranium and thorium series and from radioactive potassium, ^{40}K. In certain areas of the world, such as Brazil, France, India, Nive Island, and the United Arab Republic, much higher amounts of these substances have been found in the soil and rock. In some of these areas, the average gamma dose rate for the year exceeds one rem. Studies have been made in an attempt to measure the average gamma dose rate to the world population. Data has been collected to make a reasonable estimate. The studies which have been made include values for dose rates both indoors and outdoors. By means of the data and the assumption that most of a person's time is spent inside buildings, the estimates were made.

The background radiation which is found in the air is due mainly to the presence of radon and thoron gas, formed as daughter products of elements of the uranium and thorium series. The decay of ^{238}U produces ^{226}Ra. ^{226}Ra emits an alpha as it decays and the gas ^{222}Rn is formed. In the thorium chain, the decay of ^{224}Ra results in the product ^{220}Rn, which is called thoron.

Since uranium and thorium are present to some extent throughout the crust of the earth, these products are being formed all the time. Since they are gases, they tend to diffuse up through the earth's surface to become airborne. In turn, the decay products of these gases attach themselves to the dust in the air. .The amount of these gases in the air depends upon the uranium and thorium content of a given area. In any given area, the weather conditions will greatly affect the concentrations of these gases.

It is also common to find that the levels indoors are higher than those outdoors. This is a function of the material of the building and the ventilation rate. In mines and other underground caverns, the concentrations have been found to be quite high. Many attempts have been made to assess the dose rate to the lungs from these products. This estimate depends heavily on the assumptions made in regard to many factors which enter into the respiratory process. Some data seems to indicate that the lungs may receive a higher dose from natural sources than the body tissue. Among other radioactive products which are found in the air are ^{14}C, ^{3}H and ^{7}Be. None of these products add a significant amount to the background dose rate.

Waterborne Radiation

Depending on the type of water supply, a number of radioisotopes may be present. For example, sea water contains large amounts of ^{40}K. On the other hand, many natural springs show amounts of uranium, thorium, and radium. Almost all water should be expected to contain certain amounts of radioactivity, since rain water will pick up radioactive substances from air, and ground water will pick up activity present in rocks or soil. The dose rate from this background source occurs as the result of uptake of these waters by ingestion. This leads to an internal exposure. Any estimate of the dose rate from this source is thus included in the estimate of the dose rate form radioactivity in the human body. The transfer of radioactive substances to the body seems to be mainly by food intake except in cases of very high water concentrations.

Fallout

Fallout is the residual radiation hazard from a nuclear explosion or a nuclear accident. It is named from the fact that it "falls out" of the atmosphere in to which it is spread during an explosion or release to the atmosphere. It is radioactive dust created when a nuclear weapon explodes or released in a nuclear facility accident. This radioactive dust is radioactive contamination, and thus a source of potential radiation exposure to man. Since fallout is a manmade source of radiation, it does not properly come under the title natural background. However, since fallout can increase the contribution due to other background sources, and will affect all people, it is included.

Because of the intense heat produced in a nuclear explosion during a very short time, matter which is in the vicinity of the bomb is quickly vaporized. This includes fission products formed in the fission process, unused bomb fuel, the bomb casing and parts, and, in short, any and all substances which happen to be around. These are caught in the fireball which expands and rises very quickly. As the fireball cools and condensation occurs, a mushroom-shape cloud is formed containing small solid particles of debris as well as small drops of water. The cloud continues to rise to a height which is a function of the bomb yield and the meteorological factors of the area. For yield in the megaton range (one megaton equals an energy release equivalent to 10^6 tons of TNT), the cloud top may reach a height of twenty-five miles. The fallout which occurs may be described as local or worldwide. The portion of debris which becomes local fallout varies from none (in the case of a high-altitude detonation) to about half (in the case of a surface detonation).

The height at which the bomb goes off is thus quite important in the case of local fallout. If the fireball touches the surface of the earth, it will carry aloft large amounts of surface matter. Also, because of the suction effect created by the rapid rise of the fireball, other matter is taken up with it. This leads to the formation of larger particles in the cloud that tend to settle out quickly.

If the wind is not too great, the fallout pattern will be roughly a circle about ground zero. Ground zero is the point on the surface directly under, at, or above the burst. Other bits of matter will fall out at various stages. The distance from ground zero at which they strike the surface and the time it takes depend upon the height from which they fall, their size, and the wind patterns at all altitudes. This results in a cigar-shaped pattern downwind of the burst point. Local fallout usually occurs within the first twenty-four hours after the blast.

If the height of the burst in such that the fireball does not touch the surface, then the debris is carried aloft and dispersed into the atmosphere. This matter then descends to earth at a later time and is called world-wide fallout. The residence time of this debris is a function of the bomb yield. For the yields in the kiloton range, the debris is not projected into the stratosphere. It is limited to a region called the troposphere, between about 30,000and 55,000 feet. In this region, there is significant turbulence as well as precipitation. The debris is removed rather quickly, from about one day to one month.

If the yield is in the megaton range, the debris is carried into the stratosphere. In this region little mixing will occur, and the absence of rain or snow prevents this matter from being washed down. The time that it takes for this debris to return to the troposphere and be washed down varies and is a function of both the height of the stratosphere to which the debris is lofted and the locale at which the burst occurs. It may take up to five years or more for this debris to return to earth.

On the other hand, for burst in the northern hemisphere in which the debris is confined to only the lower part of the stratosphere, the half-residence time is thought to be less than one year. The half- residence time means the time for one-half of the debris to be removed from the stratosphere.

In all, there are more than two hundred fission products which result form a nuclear blast. The half-life of each of these products covers the range from a fraction of a second to millions of years. Local fallout will contain most of these products. Because of the time delay in the appearance of worldwide fallout, only a few of these products are important due to decay.

Since local fallout is confined to a relatively small area, its effect on the human population can be negated by the proper choice of test sites, weather conditions and type of burst. The fallout of interest from the standpoint of possible effects on man due to testing is world-wide fallout. It should be noted that in a nuclear war, local fallout would by far present the most danger.

A number of factors must be considered when one attempts to assess the hazard from world-wide fallout. Many fission products decay out in transit. Others, because they are produced in such small amounts, are diluted so that they do not produce much of an effect. Also, once fallout does arrive, there must be a transfer to the body and absorption into the organs. All these factors combine to limit the number of fission products which may have an effect on man.

The main nuclides that will affect man are ^{131}I, ^{89}Sr, ^{90}Sr, and ^{137}Cs. Another product, ^{14}C, which is produced by neutron absorption by nitrogen atoms in air, is also of interest. Both ^{131}I and ^{89}Sr, because of their short half-lives are of concern only as short-term hazards. On the other hand, ^{90}Sr, ^{137}Cs, and ^{14}C are important from the standpoint of long-term hazards. At the present time, the impact of world-wide fallout on natural background levels has been quite small. Thus, the contribution to the background dose rate from testing of nuclear weapons is very low. Danger would come from a large increase in the fission product inventory in the stratosphere. This condition could result from large-scale, long-term atmosphere testing of weapons.

Since small amounts of radioactive substances are found throughout the world in soil and water, some of this activity is transferred to man by way of the food-chain cycle. A number of studies have been made to try to find a correlation between the amount in soil and that in man. In the human body, ^{40}K, ^{226}Ra, ^{228}Ra and ^{14}C are present. Of these, ^{40}K is the most abundant. The amount of food varies greatly, so that intake is quite dependent on diet.

Most of the ^{226}Ra which is taken into the body will be found in the skeleton. Much data has been gathered on the total amount in humans, and the present assumed concentration is about seventy-five microcuries. Of this amount, eighty per cent is assumed to be in the skeleton. The amount of ^{228}Ra is approximately fifty microcuries. The average whole-body content of carbon is approximately eighteen per cent. However, ^{14}C is present in normal carbon only to a very small extent, so that only a small amount of ^{14}C is present. The average dose rate from ^{14}C turns out to be about one mrem per year to the whole body. If atmospheric fallout continues to increase the amount of ^{14}C in the environment, this value will go up.

Between 1945 and 1980, the 541 atmospheric nuclear tests that were performed together yielded about 3 tons of plutonium in the atmosphere. The average individual dose of radiation from all these nuclear explosions, accumulated between 1945 and 1998, was about 1 mSv (100 mrem). This was less than 1% of the natural dose for that period.

The survivors of the atomic bombing of Hiroshima and Nagasaki received instantaneous radiation doses of less than 200 mSv (20 rem).

The 1986–95 average radiation doses from the Chernobyl fallout ranged between 6 and 60 millisieverts (600 and 6,000 mrem). The Chernobyl accident contributed only a tiny increase of less than 0.1% to the world's fallout. In comparison, the world's average individual lifetime dose due to natural background radiation is about 150 mSv (15,000 mrem). In the contaminated regions around Chernobyl in the former Soviet Union, the lifetime dose is 210 mSv (21,000 mrem). However, in many regions of the world, the lifetime dose is about 1000 mSv (100,000 mrem).

The individual dose rate of natural radiation the average inhabitant of Earth receives is about 2.2 mSv (220 mrem) per year. Approximately 100 million people receive more than 1 mSv (100 mrem) per year, and two million people receive more than 5 mSv (500 mrem)per year.

Data on the exposure from natural and man-made radiation sources can be found in the following documents: 1) United Nations Scientific Committee on the Effects of Atomic Radiation. Sources and Effects of Ionizing Radiation. New York: United Nations Press, 1993.

2) United Nations Scientific Committee on the Effects of
Atomic Radiation. <u>Sources, Effects and Risks of Ionizing
Radiation. Annex F--Radiation Carcinogenesis in Man</u>. New
York: United Nations Press, 1988.

Data in the table below are based on the conclusions in
these 1988 and 1993 reports of the United Nations Scientific
Committees on the Effects of Atomic Radiation
(UNSCEAR).

Source	Dose Equivalent		Effective Dose Equivalent	
	mSv	mrem	mSv	%
Natural Radiation				
Radon	24	2400	2.0	55
Cosmic	0.27	27	0.27	8
Terrestrial	0.28	28	0.28	8
Internal	0.39	39	0.39	11
Total Natural	-	-	**3.0**	**82**
Medical X-ray diagnosis	0.39	39	0.39	11
Nuclear medicine	0.14	14	0.14	4
Consumer products	0,10	10	0.10	3.0
Other				
Occupational	0.009	0.9	<0.01	<0.3
Nuclear fuel cycle	<0.01	<1.0	<0.01	<0.03
Fallout	<0.01	<31.0	<0.01	<0.03
Miscellaneous	<0.01	<1.0	<0.01	<0.03
Total Artificial	-	-	**0.63**	**18**
Total	-	-	**3.63**	**100**

CHAPTER VII

Personnel Monitoring

Personnel monitoring is used to ensure that an individual is not exposed beyond the regulatory limits or at any unnecessary level. The object is to restrict the risk of adverse health effects. Carcinogenesis is believed to be the major somatic, stochastic risk of radiation exposure at low doses. With the present operating practice that exposure to radiation should be kept as low as reasonably achievable, the maintenance of personnel dosimetry records gains importance.

ALARA (acronym for "as low as is reasonably achievable") is conceptual radiation exposure guideline with the intent to encourage protection practices that are better than any prescribed standard. It means making every reasonable effort to maintain exposures to radiation as far below the dose limits in this part as is practical consistent with the purpose for which the activity is undertaken, taking into account the state of technology, the economics of improvements in relation to state of technology, the economics of improvements in relation to benefits to the public health and safety, and other societal and socioeconomic considerations, and in relation to utilization of nuclear energy and radioactive materials in the public interest.

Radiation

Survey means an evaluation of the radiological conditions and potential hazards incident to the production, use, transfer, release, disposal, or presence of radioactive material or other sources of radiation. When appropriate, such an evaluation includes a physical survey of the location of radioactive material and measurements or calculations of levels of radiation, or concentrations or quantities of radioactive contamination present. If the radiation measured is above normal background radiation, appropriate action must be taken to ensure safety.

Radiation area means an area, accessible to individuals, in which radiation levels could result in an individual receiving a dose equivalent in excess of 0.005 rem (0.05 mSv) in 1 hour at 30 centimeters from the radiation source or from any surface that the radiation penetrates.

Contamination

When a radioactive substance is being handled, processed, or used for any purpose, there is a risk that some of it will escape and be deposited on neighboring surfaces. It is like walking in mud and then coming into a building, one leaves tracks of mud. Only with radiation one does not see the contamination. Contamination behaves just as any dust-like material and can be spread from one area or object to another by tracking, smearing, or becoming airborne.

Radioactive *contamination* is deposition of radioactive material in any place where it is not desired, particularly where its presence may be harmful. Contamination can be anywhere on the body and can be transfered.to places gone or things touched. The only way to know whether or not contamination is present on clothing, equipment, or body is by monitoring with radiation detection equipment.

Zoning is a technique used to contain contamination and prevent further spreading. The technique defines a border to an area where undesirable levels of contamination exist. This border is outlined with a zone sign and radiation rope (magenta and yellow) or a painted line is used in some facilities. A step-off pad is used as a means of entering and exiting the zone to prevent spread of contamination at this point. Zones refer to different levels of radioactive contamination in contamination areas.

A *contamination area* is any area where radioactive materials (dust, dirt, etc.) are in significant amounts that could be picked up and tracked to other areas. This should not be confused with a radiation area. A *radiation area* is any area where the radiation field is five mrem per hour or any area where a person working for forty hours could accumulate 100 mrem. A *high radiation area* is any area where the radiation field exceeds 100 mrem per hour. These are important definitions and should be common knowledge to personnel working in the nuclear industry.

Radioactive contamination can enter the body through ingestion, inhalation, absorption, or injection. For this reason, it is important to use personal protective equipment when working with radioactive materials. To prevent the body surfaces from becoming contaminated, special protective clothing is issued for wear in all contamination zones. This protective clothing is also called anti-contamination clothing or anti-C's. The protective clothing requirements will not be the same for all zones and all types of work.

For work with solid radioactive contamination, canvas, cotton, or paper protective clothing is usually required. For dealing with contaminated liquids, waterproof clothing is required. To provide protection against breathing airborne contamination, respiratory protection devices are available. The type of protective clothing issued will depend on the amount of contamination present (or suspected to be present).

Considerable care must be taken when contaminated or potentially contaminated protective clothing is removed, or skin contamination may result. Employees occasionally receive skin contamination even when wearing prescribed protective clothing. *Decontamination* of external contamination is often as simple as removing contaminated clothing and cleaning contaminated skin. In most cases the contamination can be removed with soap and water. Even so, skin decontamination should be performed only by qualified personnel except in emergencies. Decontamination of personnel is usually performed by health physics personnel.

More serious than skin contamination is the problem of contaminated wounds and injuries. Wounds or injuries caused by contaminated objects or occurring in contaminated work areas provide a direct route for radioisotopes to enter the body. All wounds and injuries occurring in a radiation zone should be reported to health physics personnel immediately. Internal decontamination can be much more difficult, depending on the radionuclide in question.

Personal clothing items worn in a contamination zone may also become contaminated and must be surrendered until thoroughly decontaminated. These contaminated articles should be controlled to prevent spread of radioactive materials to clean areas or even public areas outside of the installation.

The problem of what to do with contaminated articles depends on the magnitude of the program and the experience of the individuals involved. These items fall into two main classes. Items which remain in a controlled area and which may be reused, and items which are no longer needed and can be safely released, after decontamination, for use in other work.

Contamination levels in a contaminated zone are usually subjected to indirect checks such as measurement of air concentrations, frequent measurements of personnel contamination, etc., so that hazards induced by the presence of the contaminated article become a part of the over-all program of control. Equipment to be transfer from one contaminated zone to another should be thoroughly surveyed before moving and, if the level of contamination is higher than the general level in the new zone, decontamination should be carried out.

Equipment which is shown to be contaminated, or which has inaccessible parts and has been in a contaminated zone, should be marked. All signs and labels designating a radiation or contamination hazard will be yellow with magenta lettering and will include a radiation symbol. If the material is to be stored or used by another group, it should bear a description of the kind and level of contamination and the date of the survey.

A conditional release procedure may provide suitable control of articles such as heavy mobile equipment which do not leave the installation, or of area or fixed equipment not entirely free of contamination but causing insignificant hazard. Some requirements for a conditional release are that the equipment is not contaminated to a level where it is a radiation hazard itself or the intended use presents no radiation hazard to informed users. The regulations for controlling the radiation or contamination are securely attached to the equipment in a prominent place. Property inventory records are maintained for each item listing its "home" location, radiation status, person responsible for control, and date of latest inventory.

If articles are to be released form the contaminated zone for use in uncontaminated areas, surface contamination must not exceed acceptable levels. A "wipe" or "smear" test is valuable for detecting the presence of loose contamination. In this test, the object is wiped with a piece of cloth, paper, or sticky tape, and the material measured on a sensitive device which will detect the radiation emitted. The degree of fixation of contamination and the mobility of the article is particularly important.

Some requirements for an unconditional release are that all accessible surfaces are free of significant contamination, as determined by surveys with sensitive alpha, beta or gamma monitoring instruments and that the inaccessible surfaces are uncontaminated. The materials of which the item is made are such as would not be likely to occlude radioactive materials. Wipe or smear tests indicate no detectable loose contamination, and there is reasonable assurance that any fixed contamination will not become loose and subject to spread at some later date.

Fixed contamination is radioactive particulate matter which has been fixed on a surface and cannot be removed by ordinary decontamination methods. This should not be confused with smearable contamination. Smearable contamination is radioactive particulate matter that has been deposited on floors and/or surfaces and which can be easily removed.

Radiation and contamination surveys are a vital part of control over personnel exposure, radioactive contamination, area containment and licensing compliance. To survey an area completely, fixed contamination and smearable contamination must be monitored. Since a smear will not remove fixed contamination, instruments must be used for a direct survey for fixed contamination. Smear surveys are taken to determine smearable contamination levels on area surfaces and equipment. There are a number of approved survey techniques. Smear surveys provide information for establishing contamination zones and prescribing precautions to be taken in transporting equipment from one area to another. This information is also used to establish protective clothing requirements.

A Radiation Study

Various quantities and types of radioactive materials are used in industry, medicine, research, and power generation. Almost any operation, in which radioactive materials are used, requires transportation at some point. There are numerous drivers who transport radioactive materials as a part of their normal job, which includes working with radioactive sources.

In a 1988 study conducted and published by this author entitled *A Comparison of Radiation Exposures of Highway Drivers from Various Types of Radioactive Materials*, (Library of Congress Registration Number: TX-2-323-952) the radiation exposures to drivers were documented in table below. This is followed by a description of the types of radioactive materials transported by these drivers.

Type of Material	Exposure(mrem/yr)
Spent Fuel	17
Low Level Waste	114
Uranium Hexafluoride	55
Radiopharmaceutical	421

Spent Nuclear Fuel also known as spent fuel or irradiated fuel is nuclear reactor fuel that has been used in a nuclear reactor and that contains large amounts of highly radioactive fission products. This "burned" or irradiated fuel no longer contributes efficiently to the nuclear chain reaction. Spent fuel is thermally hot and highly radioactive.

Low level waste is radioactive waste that includes cleanup and decontamination materials, contaminated wiping rags, protective clothing, vials, needles, test tubes and other contaminated medical wastes.

Uranium Hexafluoride (UF_6) is a corrosive chemical compound in the nuclear fuel cycle. At normal atmospheric temperatures, UF_6 is a clear, crystalline solid, but above 234 degrees F, UF_6 can be converted into gas.

Radiopharmaceutical (radioactive pharmaceutical) is a material containing radioisotopes used in medical diagnosis or therapy.

CHAPTER VIII

Radiation Instrumentation

Since radiation cannot be detected with the senses, a substance must be used to detect it indirectly. Instruments are used to detect the presence of radiation by the interaction of the radiation with the instrument. The part of the instrument that converts the interaction of radiation into a measurable signal is called the detector.

Many radiation detection instruments respond to the ionization produced by radiation passing through them. These include ion chambers, proportional counters, and Geiger-Mueller counters. These are gas detectors.

A different method of radiation detection is using solid state detectors. Diffused junction and surface-barrier detectors are examples of solid state detectors. Another type of detector is a scintillation detector. The may use organic or inorganic crystals. Examples of organic scintillators used are hydrocarbons and may be solids or liquids. Examples of inorganic scintillators are sodium iodide and zinc sulfide detectors. Lastly, there are neutron detectors. All of these different detectors will be discussed below.

Basic Nuclear Electronics

There are parts to counting instruments that are common to all systems. Some systems need each one of these components and other requires only a few. This depends on the particular detector used. A typical counting system consists of a detector, preamplifier, linear amplifier, discriminator, scaler, timer,

The *detector* is where the presence of radiation is converted into an electrical signal. Specific detectors will be discussed in detail later in this chapter. The *preamp* is a device that provides impedance matching, amplification, and often, charge integration of a signal before transmission to the main amplifier. The *amplifier* is a device, whose output signal is greater than, but proportional to, its input signal. A *scaler* accumulates the input pulses. This is commonly a pulse counter. The scaler accumulates pulses and displays the running total in base ten forms. The timer is used to count the duration of the pulse-counting experiment.

The Gas Amplification Curve

The figure below is the Gas Amplification Curve. It shows the relationship between the applied voltage and the pulse size. The magnitude of the voltage applied to the electrode is one or several factors that affect the number of electrons collected on the anode and the resulting charge. The gas amplification curve shows six regions. These regions are the recombination region, the ionization chamber region, the proportional region, the limited proportional region, the Geiger-Mueller region, and the continuous discharge region.

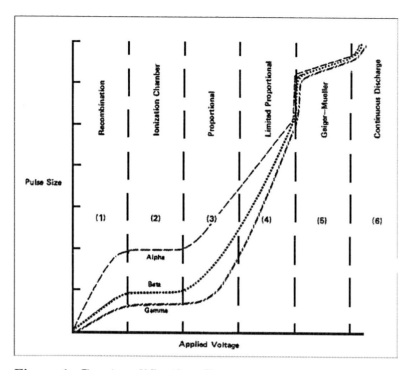

Figure 1: Gas Amplification Curve

In the *recombination region*, the voltage across the electrodes is very low, and the force between the ions and the electrodes is not great. Most of the positive and negative ions produced by the radiation are attracted to each other, rather than to the electrodes, so they recombine.

At a higher voltage in the *ionization chamber region*, the force of attraction between the ions and the electrodes is strong enough to cause all of the electrons produced by the

75

incident radiation to be collected on the anode. At this point the number of electrons collected at the anode is a function of the amount of ionization in the chamber. Three curves are shown in this region. Since alpha particles create a larger number of ion pairs per unit path length than the other radiation do, more electrons are collected on the anode and a larger pulse is produced in the external circuit. The pulse height for beta particles, which create fewer ion pairs than alphas, is slightly smaller. The pulse height for gamma photons is the smallest. Thus, in the ionization region different types of radiations can be distinguished from each other because of the different pulse heights produced in the external circuit.

In the *proportional region*, the number of ions pairs collected is larger than the number of primary ion pairs formed by the incident radiation. At high voltages, the primary negative ions or electrons are accelerated toward the anode fast enough to cause additional ionization of the gas, creating secondary ion pairs. These secondary ion pairs may also cause farther ionization. This multiplication or avalanche of electrons moving toward the anode is called gas amplification. In the proportional region, the total number of ion pairs eventually formed is proportional to the number of primary ion pairs formed by the incident radiation. Detectors that operate in this region can distinguish between alpha, beta, and gamma radiations.

The *limited proportional region* is the upper range of the proportional region. This region provides no useful purpose for radiation measurement.

In the *Geiger-Mueller region*, the gas amplification is so extensive that an avalanche of electrons spreads along the entire length of the instrument's anode. All pulses are the same size, regardless of the type of radiation that enters the detector. A detector that operates in the Geiger-Mueller region can not distinguish between the different types of radiation.

The *continuous discharge region* is the region in which the voltage is increased beyond the Geiger-Mueller region and arcing occurs across the electrodes. Pulses are registered continuously even if no radiation is present. No instruments are operated in this region, since permanent damage can result in a short time.

There are three types of ionization instruments commonly used are ionization chambers, proportional counters, and Geiger-Mueller counters. These instruments correspond to the three regions of the gas amplification curve in which radiation can be detected.

Ionization Chambers

One of the oldest devices used to detect radiation is the gas filled chamber. If the chamber is filled with a gas, *i.e.*, air other gas mixture, radiation passes through the chamber wall and produces ionization inside. If a thin metal wire is placed inside the chamber and connected so that a potential difference or voltage exists, a two electrode, gas filled detector is formed.

The outer wall of the chamber is negatively charged while the center wire is positively charged. The positive and negative ions form when radiation passes through the chamber are attracted by the oppositely charged electrode and the chamber wall. Positive charges move to the outer wall; negative charges move to the electrode. When the charges strike the electrode and outer wall, they cause a slight drop in the circuit voltage. The change in voltage is momentary and the voltage drop is called a pulse. For every radiation event that forms ion pairs in the chamber, there is a dip in voltage, hence a pulse. The size of the pulse depends upon how many ions are attracted to the electrode and the chamber wall to make the voltage drop. The number of ions pairs formed in a given volume of a substance for a given type of radiation is a fraction of the energy of the radiation and the nature of the material through which it is passing.

In a gas-filled ionization chamber, the voltage between the electrodes is increased until all ion pairs produced by the impinging radiation are collected. However, the voltage remains below that required to produce additional ion pairs as the ions pairs produced by the radiation interactions migrate to the collecting electrodes. Consequently, the electrodes receive only ions pairs that result directly from interactions of ionizing radiation with the gas in the chamber.

Proportional Counter

The proportional counter is a metal container of counting gas, with an electrode in the center with a high voltage. When radiation enters the detector, electrons are swept to the center electrode and are collected to make a pulse proportional to the incident radiation energy.

The operating voltage of a proportional counter depends upon the gas mixture and the geometry. At too low a voltage, the electrons may recombine with the atoms before reaching the center electrode. At too high a voltage, the electrons may eject large numbers of other electrons from the atoms as they are accelerated toward the center electrode producing a pulse independent of the initial radiation energy. At still higher voltages there is continuous discharge of electrons.

In the proportional region, the size of the pulse is a function of the detector voltage, and it is proportional to the number of primary ion pairs formed. Because of the differences in total ionization within the chamber, alpha particles produce larger pulses than beta particles of the same energy. This region of proportionality between pulse size and particle size is the region where alpha and beta proportional counters are operated.

In the proportional region, the pulses produced by the heavier alpha particles are larger than the particles produced by beta particles, because alpha particles produce far more primary ion than beta particles. For a given voltage, the gas amplification factor for alpha and beta particles is the same size which makes the resultant pulse size totally dependent upon the number of primary ions formed. Since alpha particles form more primary ions, its pulse size will be larger. Because of the difference in pulse size between the two radiations, their pulses are easily electronically distinguishable. The electronics of some proportional counters are designed for separate counting of alpha and beta particles by utilizing their difference in pulse size.

Geiger-Mueller (GM) Counters

When voltage is increased beyond the limited proportional region in the gas amplification curve, another plateau region, or region where pulse size does not change with increasing voltage, is found. This is because the voltage is so great and the gas amplification factor is so high that a single event entering the detector and causing any primary ionization results in a complete ionization of all the gas in the chamber. Further, secondary ionization is not possible. Pulse size is no longer dependent upon the number of primary ions formed. The pulse size is always the same regardless of the number of primary ions formed or the energy or size of the radiation causing the ionization. Therefore, instruments operating in this region, called the Geiger-Mueller region, have no ability to distinguish between alpha, beta, and gamma radiation but can merely indicate the presence of radioactivity.

If the voltage is increased beyond the Geiger-Mueller region, an arc is formed and a continuous discharge occurs. The electrodes can be severely damaged if operated in this region. This region is called the continuous discharge region.

A GM counter is usually a cylindrical metal tube with an electrode in the center, filled with a gas mixture. Incident radiation ejects electrons from atoms, leaving positive ions and electrons. The electrons and ions are accelerated toward the center electrode and the outer cathode respectively. If the accelerating voltage is high enough, the electrons collide with other electrons at high enough energy to eject more electrons. The avalanche of electrons that occurs produces a pulse that is now constant in amplitude, unrelated to the energy of the initial radiation. GM detectors are very sensitive to all different types of radiation but cannot discriminate between them. Because of the large size of the output pulse, the GM detector requires much less external amplification.

Solid State Detectors

One type of solid state detector is the semiconductor detector. A semiconductor detector is especially useful for measurement of charged particles such as electrons, protons, and alphas. These materials can be either a good conductor of electric current or a good insulator depending on the structure of the bonds in a given crystal substance. A semiconductor detector acts as a solid state ionization chamber. The ionizing particle interacts with atoms in the sensitive volume of the detector to produce electrons by ionization. The collection of the ions leads to an output pulse. In contrast to the relatively high mean ionization energy of 30-35 electron volts (eV) for most counting gases, a mean energy expenditure of only about 2.94 eV is required to produce an ionizing event in a germanium semiconductor detector.

The lithium-drifted germanium detector {Ge(Li)} (also called "jelly" detector) is made by first doping germanium with an acceptor impurity making it P-type material. Lithium metal is then evaporated onto the surface of the crystal with the temperature raised to about 400 degrees Centigrade where diffusion initially takes place. Lithium has a Z number of three and one valence electron. Therefore, it is ionized very easily which causes it to immediately begin filling electron holes. Due to the ease at which the lithium drifts through the crystal, a Ge(Li) crystal must be kept at a cryogenic temperature. This is accomplished by putting the crystal in contact with a copper rod which conducts the cold from a dewar of liquid nitrogen. If it is not kept cold, the lithium will simply drift out of the crystal.

The semiconductor surface barrier detector is a wafer of either silicon or germanium that is doped with a small amount of impurity atoms. A very thin layer of gold is applied to one side to make a p-n junction. The bias voltage is applied in reverse direction to back bias the detector. The only current that flows is a small thermal leakage current.

The impurity atoms act as essentially free charge carriers (electrons or holds). The reverse bias acts to form a depletion region in which there are no free charges. To function as a particle detector, the depletion region should be greater than the range of particles being detected. In the detection process the particle is stopped in the depletion region, forming electron hole pairs in the process. The energy necessary to form a single hole pair depends on the detector material. It is essentially independent of the energy of the incoming particle. The number of electron-hole pairs ultimately found is directly proportional to the energy of the stopped particle. The electric field in the region due to the detector bias sweeps the electrons to one terminal and the holes to the other. It is this charge pulse that is integrated in a charge sensitive preamplifier to yield the observed voltage pulse.

The width of the depletion region depends upon the applied bias voltage, so that higher voltages give a thicker region, capable of stopping more energetic particles. The capacitance of the detector depends upon the width of the depletion region and the size (area) of the wafer, so detector bias will affect the capacitance (and response) of the detector. The detector capacitance is reduced at higher voltages so that the lowest noise and best resolution are obtained at the maximum voltage that can be placed on the detector.

Scintillation Detectors

Scintillation detectors are based on the property of certain substances to absorb energy from high energy radiation and re-emit some of this energy as visible or near visible electromagnetic radiation (light). In a scintillation crystal, light is released as radiation is absorbed. The light impinges upon a photosensitive surface in a photomultiplier tube. Electrons released from this surface constitute an electric signal. Scintillation detectors may be used to detect particulate radiation as well as x-ray and gamma photons.

When an x-ray or gamma ray interacts within a scintillation crystal, electrons are raised from one energy state to a state of higher energy. The number of electrons raised to a higher energy level depends upon the energy deposited in the crystal by the incident photon. Light is released as these electrons return almost instantaneously to the lower energy state. The photons of light are transmitted through the transparent crystal and are directed upon the photosensitive cathode (photocathode) of a photomultiplier tube. If the wavelength of light striking the photocathode matches the spectral sensitivity of this photosensitive surface, then electrons are ejected. The number of electrons is multiplied by the various stages (dynodes) of the photomultiplier tube, and a signal is provided at the photomultiplier anode which may be amplified electronically and counted. The size of the signal at the anode is proportional to the energy dissipated in the detector by the incident radiation.

Sodium iodide is an alkali halide crystal often used as a scintillation crystal. Alkali halide crystals are used because the probabilities of photoelectric interactions are increased by the presence of the high-Z halide component. The efficiency of a crystal for detecting x-ray and gamma photons increases with the size of the crystal. To be used as a scintillation detector, an alkali halide crystal must be "activated" with an impurity. This impurity is thallium iodide, and the crystals are denoted as NaI(Tl).

Another example of an inorganic crystal scintillator is zinc sulfide (ZnS). This crystal is commonly used for alpha detection and isotopic analysis of alpha emitters.

Organic liquid scintillators are particularly useful for detecting low energy beta. In these detectors, the material to be counted is mixed with the liquid scintillator and placed in a vial surrounded by light sensitive photocathodes. Light is produced within the vial containing the scintillator. The rest of the process of converting the light into a usable pulse is the same process as described in this section. Organic scintillators are also very useful in the detection of neutrons as they have a high hydrogen content, but their efficiency for gamma detection is low.

The scintillation detector is comprised of several components. The component where incident radiation interacts to produce light is known as the scintillator or phosphor. The light pipe, if used, provides several important functions in the scintillation system. This device acts as an "optical coupler" to focus the light found in the phosphor onto the photocathode. This helps to prevent the trapping of light in the phosphor. If effectively spreads the light over a greater surface of the photocathode. It can transmit through long distances around gradual bends without appreciable loss if it is necessary to have the phosphor and photocathode separated.

The photocathode is the part of the multiplier tube where light from the phosphor causes the production of free electrons. It must have a high performance for photoelectric emissions *i.e.*, converts light into electrons. Also, it must be receptive to the wavelength of light emitted from the phosphor.

The photomultiplier receives the electrons produced in the photocathode and multiplies them so that an electric pulse can be detected. Near the photocathode is the first of a series of collecting electrodes called dynodes. The photomultiplier tube may contain approximately ten dynodes. Each dynode is maintained at a positive voltage potential with respect to the dynode above it so that electrons are attracted to and strike the first dynode causing more electrons to be released than struck it. This event is repeated with each dynode such that an amplification results.

The number of electrons freed at each dynode depends upon the amount of energy acquired by the electrons striking the dynode. This, in turn, depends upon the voltage difference between each dynode. A typical amplification factor for a photomultiplier tube is 10^6. That is, for every electron emitted at the photocathode, 10^6 (1,000,000) electrons are collected at the anode or output of the photomultiplier.

The preamplifier and linear amplifier both magnify the electrical pulse that is formed in the photomultiplier tube so that the pulse can be detected. With the preceding discussion in mind, it is evident that for each ionizing event that looses energy in the phosphor a discrete electrical pulse will appear at the anode of the photomultiplier tube. The pulse size will be proportional to the energy of the event deposited in the phosphor which is what makes scintillation detectors useful for isotopic spectrum analysis.

Neutron Detectors

Since neutrons are neutral particles, they are not directly detectable. The types of interactions which neutrons undergo depend quite strongly on the energy of the neutron. As in the case with gamma rays, certain interactions predominate depending on energy. It is advantageous to treat neutrons in terms of the energy range in which they predominate.

When neutrons are slowed down so that they are in thermal equilibrium with matter, they have speeds comparable to gas molecules at room temperature. In this case, the most probable velocity is about 2200meters/second. These are called *thermal neutrons*. They have energies of about 0.025 eV. *Intermediate neutrons* or "resonance neutrons" have an energy region from 0.5 eV to 10 keV. *Fast neutrons* have a range in energy from 10 keV 10 MeV. *Relativistic neutrons* have a energy range of greater than 10 MeV.

For most neutron detectors, the detection of neutrons depends on the detection of some other form of radiation which is easily detectable. The presence of this other radiation must be directly attributable to the presence of neutrons. Generally, a neutron must be slowed down to thermal energies before it can be absorbed by a nucleus of an atom. The nucleus then emits an ionizing radiation that can be readily detected. Some nuclei will absorb thermal neutrons more readily than others. These nuclei are said to have a high thermal neutron cross-section. Since all neutrons are not thermal, a way to thermalize and capture them and detect the resultant emitted ionizing radiation is necessary.

For fast neutrons, *elastic scattering* is the predominant mode of interaction. Because the neutron has no charge, it does not interact with the electric field of a nucleus and can pass very close to charged particles. For this reason, one can view neutron interactions as collisions with nuclei. An elastic collision can be thought of as a "billiard-ball" type of collision in which energy and momentum are conserved. The loss of energy by a neutron in an elastic collision is greatest when the colliding particles have equal mass. Thus, a neutron will lose the most energy in a collision with a proton (hydrogen nucleus). The average fraction of energy lost is about the same for each collision. As the mass of the target becomes very large, the neutron will lose hardly any of its energy. As an example, one can think of a BB thrown against a bowling ball. Paraffin makes an excellent neutron moderator (or material that will slow down neutrons) because of the abundance of hydrogen atoms.

In the energy range above 0.5 MeV, *inelastic scattering* begins to occur. In the process, the neutron raises the nucleus to an excited state and comes off with a loss in energy. The excited nucleus often returns to ground state by emitting the excess energy as a gamma ray. For the process to occur, the neutron must supply the excitation energy to the nucleus. In heavy elements, the first excitation state is about 100 keV above the ground state. For light elements, this state may be at 3 or 4 MeV. This process, then, is more predominant for heavier nuclei and neutrons of higher energy (> 1 MeV). Near the upper end of the fast neutron range, inelastic scattering begins to occur as frequently as elastic scattering.

The process of elastic scattering is still dominant for intermediate neutrons. The phenomenon of resonance absorption or *resonance capture* also occurs in this region. The probability of absorption increases greatly when a neutron has an energy which is equal to a nuclear energy level of the absorbing substance. Thus, the substance will absorb more neutrons of this energy than of energy either slightly higher or lower. When neutron energy becomes less than about 100 eV, capture becomes an important process.

As the neutron is further decreased, it approaches the thermal neutron range. The dominant process for thermal neutrons is *thermal capture* in which the neutron becomes part of the absorbing nucleus. The compound nucleus thus formed must then get rid of the excess energy, usually by emission of gamma rays. This is called radioactive capture. This reaction occurs in a neutron detector where helium gas is placed inside an ionization chamber covered with polyethelene. The neutrons are moderated by the hydrogen atoms in the polyethelene and then undergo thermal capture reactions with the helium. The resulting protons are easily detected.

In one type of neutron detector that is commonly called a "rem ball", there is a 9-inch diameter, cadmium loaded, polyethelene sphere with a BF_3 tube in the center. When a neutron enters the sphere, those of moderate or high energy are slowed down by elastic collisions with the hydrogen atoms in the polyethelene. Thermal neutrons entering the sphere are not appreciable affected by the polyethelene and pass on toward the center. The cadmium covering the BF_3 tube in the sphere is approximately 1.1 millimeters thick and covers the sphere in "orange peel" strips with small gaps between them. Therefore, most of the thermalized neutrons are captured by the cadmium and do not get counted. The purpose of the cadmium strips is to provide a nearly linear dose response over a wide range of neutron energies. When a neutron enters the BF_3 detector and interacts with a ^{10}B atom, an alpha particle is emitted by the ^{10}B nucleus. The ionization resulting from the alpha particle is detected as a pulse by the instrument. The nicest characteristic of this neutron detector is that it reads out directly in rem/hr. Therefore, no conversions are necessary to obtain the dose as is the case with most other neutron detectors.

Multichannel Analyzer

The multichannel analyzer is literally like a whole series of single channel analyzers. When a pulse is received, it is sent automatically to the channel for whose discriminator settings it satisfies. A given pulse can satisfy the discriminator setting for only one channel. A multichannel takes a wide energy range (0 to several million electron volts or MeV) and divides it equally into channels (may vary from 256 to 4096 or more). The number of channels is always equal to 2 to some integral power (2^x). For each successive channel, the low level discriminator setting is equal to the previous channel high level discriminator setting. Therefore, pulses in a channel are equal to the energy deposited in the detector within a very narrow range. Instead of making a series of counts using a series of settings to obtain one spectrum with a single channel analyzer, only one count is necessary using a multichannel analyzer. Counting continues for a duration determined by the experiment until an energy distribution spectrum is accumulated. This process is called pulse height analysis.

Counting Times

Individual radioactive atoms decay at random, emitting radiation at a time and in a direction that cannot be predicted. However, when there are many decaying atoms, the average time of decay and the average number in a given direction can be determined. Because of the variations in time and direction of decay, successive measurements of the counts in a given time will not be exactly the same. The values obtained will be distributed about a mean value. The accuracy in determining the average number of counts in a small interval is related to the number of counts. A long counting time can be considered as a sequence of short counting times so that variation above and below the average will tend to cancel out.

CHAPTER IX

Historical Events

On November 8, 1895, German physics professor Wilhelm Conrad Roentgen (1845-1923) discovered rays that could travel through solid wood or flesh.

On January 12, 1896, only a few days after the announcement of Roentgen's work, Emil Grubbe, a Chicago electrotherapist, irradiated a woman with a recurrent cancer of the breast.

In 1896, a French physicist, Antoine Henri Becquerel (1852-1908), discovered that the rays emitted by uranium caused gases to ionize and that they differed from X-rays in that they could be deflected by electric or magnetic fields.

On February 3, 1896, Dr. Edwin Frost (1866-1935) made the first diagnostic radiograph in the U.S. at Dartmouth.

In April of 1896, The Archives of Clinical Skiagraphy, issued in London, was the first widely-read journal of radiology.

In May of 1897, the American X-Ray Journal was first published by St. Louis physician and entrepreneur Heber Robarts, M.D. Originally the official origin of the American Roentgen Ray Society.

In 1898, Madame Marie Sklodowska-Curie (1867-1934) and her husband, Pierre Curie (1859-1906), discovered two radioactive elements, radium and polonium.

In 1901, Wilhelm Conrad Roentgen received the Nobel Prize for physics "in recognition of the extraordinary services he has rendered by the discovery of the remarkable rays subsequently named after him."

In 1903, Marie and Pierre Curie received the Nobel Prize for physics "in recognition of the extraordinary services they have rendered by their joint researches on the radiation phenomena discovered by Professor Henri Becquerel" and Henri Becquerel received the Nobel Prize for physics "in recognition of the extraordinary services he has rendered by his discovery of spontaneous radioactivity." Marie was granted her doctorate the same year.

In 1905, Albert Einstein (1879-1955) showed that energy and mass were actually different aspects of the same thing related by $E=mc^2$ where E is energy, m is mass, and c is the speed of light.

In 1908, Ernest Rutherford (1871-1937) won the Nobel Prize in chemistry for "for his investigations into the disintegration of the elements, and the chemistry of radioactive substances." He is considered the father of nuclear physics. The alpha particle, beta particle and proton were particles named and characterized by him.

In 1911, Marie received her second Nobel Prize, this time in chemistry "in recognition of her services to the advancement of chemistry by the discovery of the elements radium and polonium, by the isolation of radium and the study of the nature and compounds of this remarkable element." She was the first person ever to receive two Nobel Prizes.

In 1921, Albert Einstein won the Nobel Prize in physics "for his services to Theoretical Physics, and especially for his discovery of the law of the photoelectric effect."

In 1922, Niels Henrik David Bohr (1885-1962) won the Nobel Prize in physics "for his services in the investigation of the structure of atoms and of the radiation emanating from them."

In 1932, Sir James Chadwick (1891-1974) proved the existence of the neutron.

In 1935, Sir James Chadwick won a Nobel Prize for physics "for the discovery of the neutron"

In 1935, Marie Curie's oldest daughter, Irene Joliot-Curie and her husband Frederic Joliot also won a Nobel Prize for Chemistry "in recognition of their synthesis of new radioactive elements". Marie Curie was the first mother-Nobel Prize Laureate of daughter-Nobel Prize Laureate.

The first successful experiment with nuclear fission was conducted in 1938 in Berlin by the German physicists Otto Hahn, Lise Meitner and Fritz Strassman.

In 1938, Enrico Fermi (1901-1954) won the Nobel Prize in physics "for his demonstrations of the existence of new radioactive elements produced by neutron irradiation, and for his related discovery of nuclear reactions brought about by slow neutrons."

In 1939, Ernest Orlando Lawrence (1901-1958) won the Nobel Prize in physics "for the invention and development of the cyclotron and for results obtained with it, especially with regard to artificial radioactive elements."

On December 2, 1942, Enrico Fermi made a chain reaction in a pile of uranium at the University of Chicago and the Nuclear Age began.

On August 6, 1945, the United States dropped an atomic bomb on Hiroshima, Japan, killing over 100,000 people. Then 3 days later on August 9, 1945, another atomic bomb was dropped on Nagasaki, Japan, killing over 40,000 people.

In 1951, Glenn Theodore Seaborg and Edwin Mattison McMillan, both from University of California at Berkeley, won the Nobel Prize in chemistry "for their discoveries in the chemistry of the transuranium elements."

Electricity was generated for the first time by a nuclear reactor on December 20, 1951 at the EBR-I experimental station. EBR-I is a Registered National Historic Landmark in the desert about 18 miles southeast of Arco, Idaho.

On June 27, 1954, the world's first nuclear power plant that generated electricity for commercial use was officially connected to the Soviet power grid at Obninsk, Kaluga Oblast, Russia.

On February 21, 1956, the second reactor for commercial purposes was Calder Hall in Sellafield, England. It was a gas-cooled reactor with a capacity of 45 MW.

The Shippingport Reactor in Beaver County, Pennsylvania was the first commercial nuclear generator to become operational in the United States. It began operating on December 2, 1957, and was in operation until October, 1982.

In 1979, an accident occurred at the Three Mile Island Nuclear Generating Station that sits on the island in the Susquehanna River near Harrisburg, Pennsylvania. Radioactive material was released to the atmosphere when the cooling system leaked. It forced tens of thousands of people to evacuate the area. The problem was solved minutes before a total meltdown would have occurred. Fortunately, there were no deaths.

In 1986, a much worse disaster struck Russia's Chernobyl nuclear power plant. In this incident, a large amount of radiation escaped from the reactor. It produced a plume of radioactive debris that drifted over parts of the western Soviet Union, Eastern Europe, Scandinavia, UK, and eastern USA. Large areas of Ukraine, Belarus, and Russia were badly contaminated, resulting in the evacuation and resettlement of roughly 200,000 people. About 60% of radioactive fallout landed in Belarus. Hundreds of thousands of people were exposed to the radiation. Several dozen died within a few days. In the years to come, thousands more may die of cancers induced by the radiation.

As of 2005, there are 441 nuclear power reactors in operation around the world. Together they produce about one-sixth of the world's electric power.

CHAPTER X

Additional Definitions

Agreement State: A state that has entered into an agreement with the U.S. Nuclear Regulatory Commission to assume regulatory responsibility for radioactive materials under Section 274 of the Atomic Energy Act of 1954 as amended.

As low as reasonably achievable (ALARA): A conceptual radiation exposure guideline with the intent to encourage protection practices that are better than any prescribed standard.

By-product Material: Radioactive material yielded in or made radioactive by exposure to radiation incident to the process of producing or utilizing special nuclear materials; tailings or waste produced by the extraction or concentration of uranium or thorium from any ore processed primarily for its source material content.

Collective Effective Dose Equivalent: The per caput dose equivalent in the whole body or any specific organ or tissue over the number of individuals exposed.

Dose: The total amount of ionizing radiation absorbed during a period of exposure.

Dose Equivalent: A term used to express the amount of effective radiation when modifying factors have been considered. It is expressed numerically in rem or severt.

Dose Rate: Radiation absorbed per unit time. May be measured in mrem/hr and severt/hr.

Dosimetry: The theory and application of the principles and techniques involved in the measurement and recording of radiation doses.

Exposure: Used as a term to express radiation dose.

Fuel Cycle: The complete series of steps involved in supplying fuel for nuclear reactors. It includes mining, refining, the original fabrication of fuel elements, their use in a reactor, and management of spent fuel and radioactive wastes.

License: A license issued under the regulations in Title 10 of the Code of Federal Regulations, Parts 30 through 35, 40, 60, 61, 70 or 72.

Licensee: The holder of a license.

Light Water Reactor (LWR): A nuclear reactor cooled and moderated by water.

Low Level Radioactive Waste: Radioactive waste including cleanup and decontamination materials, contaminated wiping rags, protective clothing, vials, needles, test tubes and other contaminated medical wastes.

Millirem (mrem): One thousandth of a rem.

Occupational Radiation Exposure: Exposure to ionizing radiation in the course of employment.

Person-rem (man-rem): The product of average dose equivalent by the number of people affected.

Personnel Monitoring: For use in this thesis, the determination of radiation dosage received by means of dosimetry devices.

Radiation: The energy emitted from a atom in the form of particles or electromagnetic waves.

Radiation Dosimeter: A device which measures the radiation dose which a person receives.

Radiation Worker: Adult who is exposed to ionizing radiation in the course of work and is under a federal or state approved radiation protection program.

Radioisotope (Radionuclide): For the purpose of transportation, these terms are synonymous and identify

112

specific isotopes of chemical elements that have radioactive properties.

Radiopharmaceutical: Short for radioactive pharmaceutical. A material containing radioisotopes used in medical diagnosis or therapy.

Rem: The input of dose equivalent. 1 rem equals 0.01 joule per kilogram. For gamma radiation consider 1 rem equals 1 R. A subunit of the rem is the millirem which equals one thousandth of a rem.

Roentgen (R): Unit of exposure to gamma radiation. A measure of the ability of gamma radiation to produce ionization in air. 1 R equals 2.6×10^{-4} coulomb per kilogram. A subunit of the R is the milliroentgen (mR) which equals one thousandth of a roentgen.

Special Nuclear Material: Plutonium and uranium enriched in U-235 or U-233 in higher enrichments which could be used to make nuclear weapons if they were available in sufficient quantity and purity.

Spent Nuclear Fuel (Spent fuel, Irradiated fuel): Nuclear reactor fuel that has been used in a nuclear reactor and that contains large amounts of highly radioactive fission products. This "burned" or irradiated fuel no longer contributes efficiently to the nuclear chain reaction. Spent fuel is thermally hot and highly radioactive.

Somatic, Stochastic Risks: Those health risks for which the probability of an occurrence, rather than the severity, is considered to be a function of dose without threshold and is limited to the exposed individual.

Source Material: Uranium and/or thorium, or ores containing by weight 0.05 percent or more uranium and/or thorium.

Unirradiated Fuel: Fresh nuclear reactor fuel or fuel which has not gone into a reactor.

Uranium Hexafloride (UF$_6$): A corrosive chemical compound in the nuclear fuel cycle. A normal atmospheric temperatures, UF$_6$ is a clear, crystalline solid, but above 234 degrees F, UF$_6$ can be converted into gas.

CPSIA information can be obtained at www.ICGtesting.com
Printed in the USA
LVOW08s1237181013

357536LV00001B/112/A